The Government Response
to the Health Committee Report on the
Electronic Patient Record

Presented to Parliament by
the Secretary of State for Health
by Command of Her Majesty
November 2007

Cm 7264

£5.15

Contents

Introduction

This Command Paper sets out the Government's response to the Health Select Committee's Sixth Report of the Session 2006/07 on the electronic patient record.

Background

The House of Commons Health Select Committee (the Committee) published its report into the Electronic Patient Record on 13 September 2007. This Command Paper sets out the Government's response to the conclusions and recommendations in that report.

The Government welcomes the report's conclusions on the potential of electronic patient records to improve healthcare services and patient safety. In particular, it agrees with the Committee's view that the implementation of electronic patient records is a 'long journey best managed by a staged and piloted development not a big bang approach'. The Government reaffirms its view that solid progress has been made on the delivery of the National Programme for IT in the NHS (the National Programme), though it accepts that delays have occurred to the delivery of some parts of the Programme. These delays are in many instances the consequences of taking longer over consultation and stakeholder engagement rather than simply delays in the production of software. In any event, the robustness of the contracts with suppliers means that the costs of any IT system delays have not been borne by the taxpayer. The Government recognises that continuing effort is needed to engage with frontline NHS staff and to communicate the Programme plans to the public.

The central vision of the National Programme is to make essential patient information available at the point of need, through the NHS Care Records Service. Initially, the National Programme included the following major core components:

- an Electronic NHS Care Records Service to improve the sharing of patients' records across the NHS with their consent;

- an Electronic Booking Service to make it easier and faster to book hospital appointments for patients;

- an Electronic Prescription Service; and

- a New National Network (N3) to provide a broadband IT infrastructure to ensure that NHS data transfer needs could be met now and in the future.

Since its initiation, a number of programmes have been added to the scope of the National Programme, in order to:

- support NHS reforms;

- improve the delivery of existing NHS IT programmes;

- ensure that information is integrated; and

- support the Cancer Strategy.

Programmes added to support NHS reforms

In support of the policy on patient choice, which was set out in *The NHS Plan* (July 2000) and extended in *Health Reform in England: Update and Next Steps* (December 2005), the proposed Electronic Booking Service was extended to provide patient choice. It was renamed as Choose and Book.

General practitioner (GP) contracts contain a Quality and Outcomes Framework of national achievement targets describing how GP practices are rewarded financially based on their achievements. The Quality Management and Analysis System (QMAS) was introduced to collect national achievement data, compute national disease prevalence rates and calculate the points and payment values earned by GP practices. QMAS also allows GP practices to analyse the data they collect about the services and quality of care they deliver.

The National Programme has also been extended to support:

- Payment by Results, announced in *NHS Financial Reforms: Introducing Payment by Results* (October 2002);

- the 18 weeks delivery programme, announced in The NHS Improvement Plan (June 2004): 'By 2008 no one will wait longer than 18 weeks from GP referral to hospital treatment';

- Practice Based Commissioning, announced in *Health Reform in England: Update and Next Steps* (December 2005); and

- NHS restructuring.

Existing NHS IT programmes incorporated into the National Programme

The following existing NHS IT programmes were incorporated into the National Programme:

- NHS Numbers for Babies, which issues an NHS number at birth, thereby enabling health episodes to be recorded on discrete personal records from the outset; and

- NHSmail, an email and national directory service for all NHS staff which is secure and can be used for the transmission of patient and clinical data.

Programmes added to ensure integrated information

The following programmes were incorporated into the National Programme because they provide the greatest value for patients when integrated with other components of the programme:

- Picture Archiving and Communication Systems (PACS), which are digital imaging systems that capture X-rays, computerised tomography (CT) scans and magnetic resonance (MR) scans electronically to aid diagnoses, were added to the National Programme in September 2004. PACS had previously been procured piecemeal by the NHS.

- The GP to GP Transfer System, which enables the electronic transfer of a patient record to the new GP practice when a patient changes their GP.

Programme added in response to the Cancer Strategy

In 2004, a national screening programme for bowel cancer was announced which would be implemented progressively across the country from April 2006. The Bowel Cancer Screening System supports this programme.

Progress on the National Programme

The National Programme has made significant progress since its inception. On a typical day in October 2007, there were:

- 250,000 prescriptions transmitted electronically, reducing errors and inefficiencies;

- 18,000 Choose and Book electronic bookings made, putting patients in charge of their care;

- over 1.4 million enquiries recorded on the Personal Demographics Service (PDS), enabling letters to be posted to the correct address and patient information to be handled more efficiently;

- over 1.7 million digital images stored on PACS;

- over 2,500 new users registered for access to the NHS Care Records Service;

- 52,000 unique, authenticated users accessing the NHS Care Records Service;

- over 1,500 new NHS secure email users registered;

- over 120,000 NHSmail users, each of whom has an email address for life, sending 1 million secure emails, one-third of which contain confidential patient information;

- 54 NHS National Network secure broadband connections installed;

- nearly 9,000 GP practices (33,000 GPs) using QMAS to deliver better care to patients under the new GP contract; and

- 1.5 million records added to the Secondary Uses Service.

In his interim report on the NHS Next Stage Review, *Our NHS Our Future* (October 2007), Professor the Lord Darzi of Denham FREng, KBE, FMedSci records that the NHS's recent investment in technology has created the opportunity to make a step change in the NHS. The introduction of the electronic patient record remains at the centre of this investment.

Response to the Committee's recommendations

Recommendation (paragraph 116)

The Committee is aware of the Department's most recent plans but is concerned that the complexity of the SCR appears to be increasing. This will make the SCR more difficult to use, particularly in emergency situations. The Department must be clear about the purpose of the SCR, and it must ensure that the record is easy to use. To this end, we recommend that the SCR include a single standardised front screen to display key health information which is vital for emergency care.

The Government accepts this recommendation. The Summary Care Record (SCR) has been designed in consultation with clinicians working in urgent care settings. There is a single standardised front screen to display key health information which is vital for emergency care. The design has been agreed with the National Clinical Reference Panel. The functionality will allow this summary information to be viewed from within unscheduled care settings, for example accident and emergency departments, walk-in centres and out-of-hours services. The first information included in the SCR will be basic information such as known allergies, known adverse reactions to medications and other substances (for example, peanuts), prescriptions issued in the past six months and repeat prescriptions that are not more than six months beyond their review date. If the SCR is developed and augmented with additional information beyond that which is currently planned, then the redesign of the screen will be agreed through the same channels.

Recommendation (paragraph 119)

The Committee considers that much of the controversy over privacy and consent arrangements for the SCR would have been avoided if Connecting for Health had communicated its plans more clearly to patients. We recommend that Connecting for Health:

- **Make clear to patients, clinicians and the public that detailed information will only be added to the SCR with explicit patient consent, that patients can see this information before it is added, and that patients can choose to have an SCR created but not accessed beyond their GP surgery; and**

- **Offer the same assurances to all patients in the SCR early adopter sites.**

The Government accepts these recommendations for the SCR early adopter programme, noting that initial work on communicating on privacy and consent in this area was carried out by both the NHS Information Authority and the NHS Modernisation Agency prior to their closure.

In the early adopter programme, where the only source of data is the GP record, the creation of an SCR containing a person's current medication, allergies and adverse reactions is a matter of informed consent supported through a public information programme. Adding the patient's significant medical history occurs only through a discussion between the patient and their GP, as does the adding of information about new health episodes.

The result of the approach taken is that patients are informed before the introduction of the SCR and may choose whether to have an SCR; may choose what is in it; may restrict who may see it; and may view it themselves through HealthSpace, a website with registration and access controls.

All the published information makes it clear that patients have a choice and that the NHS will continue to provide the best care that it can, irrespective of whether patients have an SCR. However, the Department of Health will take all reasonable steps to ensure that these intentions are understood.

The public information programme seeks to reach patients with timely information and support their choices before local implementation of the SCR and has therefore been focused on the early adopter sites. Experience in these sites will be evaluated independently and changes to the communications will be made where necessary.

The SCR early adopter programme will provide experience and learning which will inform the SCR's future development, including the best ways of engaging individual citizens in the choices available to them.

Recommendation (paragraph 121)

"Sealed envelopes" are a vital mechanism if sensitive information is to be held on the SCR. We recommend that:

- **The right to break the seal protecting information in "sealed envelopes" should only be held by patients themselves, except where there is a legal requirement to override this measure; and**

- **Information in "sealed envelopes" should not be made available to the Secondary Uses Service under any circumstances; this will allow patients to prevent data being used for research purposes without their consent.**

The Government accepts the first of these recommendations. Patient-sealed envelopes provide the mechanism whereby patients can restrict access to the parts of their SCR they consider to be particularly sensitive. Patients will be able to request that parts of their record are either 'sealed' or 'sealed and locked'. These procedures form a level of access control deployed at the direction of the patient, not the NHS.

Sealed information will be recorded on the SCR and system users will be aware that some information has been sealed. However, access to the sealed information from outside of the team recording it will be obtainable only with the patient's consent or in exceptional circumstances. Only those users with the necessary privileges will be able to gain temporary access to sealed information without the patient's consent. A privacy officer will be alerted to the temporary access by any user and patients registered with HealthSpace will receive a notification when access permissions are changed or when temporary access is gained.

Sealed and locked information cannot be accessed outside of the team that recorded it. Users who do not have permission to access the sealed and locked information will be unaware of its presence.

The circumstances where patient-identifiable sealed and locked information may be lawfully disclosed by the clinical team that has access to it, and the circumstances where patient-identifiable information that is simply 'sealed' can be accessed by those outside of the team that recorded it, without the patient's consent, are essentially the same. They are limited to circumstances where the information is required by law or where a significant public interest justification exists (for example, serious crime, child protection etc).

The Government does not accept the second of the recommendations. Patient consent to the use of anonymised or effectively pseudonymised data is not required by law and the use of such data for secondary uses, including research, is both accepted and actively promoted by the relevant professional and regulatory bodies. The Committee received strong evidence on the need for health information to be made available for research from a number of organisations. The design of the Secondary Uses Service ensures that patient confidentiality is protected.

Recommendation (paragraph 122)

HealthSpace is an excellent addition to the SCR programme and has huge potential to improve the safety and efficiency of care by allowing patients to check the accuracy of their SCR and to access detailed information about their own health. In order to take fuller advantage of HealthSpace, we recommend that Connecting for Health:

- **Trial the use of HealthSpace for patients, particularly those with long-term conditions, to record their own measurements of key health information;**

- **Ensure that HealthSpace allows patients to view audit trails, showing who has accessed their SCR record and under what circumstances, and offers mechanisms for investigating inappropriate access;**

- **Promote the use of HealthSpace, monitor levels of uptake, and ensure that there is equitable access across the country and that coercive access is prevented; and**

- **Commission an independent evaluation of HealthSpace once the system is widely available.**

The Government welcomes the Committee's support for HealthSpace, which is a secure online personal health organiser where patients can store their personal health information, such as height, weight and blood pressure as well as viewing their SCR.

The Government accepts in principle the recommendation to trial the use of HealthSpace for patients, particularly those with long-term conditions, to record their own measurements of key health information. NHS Connecting for Health has started work with the Patient Reference Panel to engage with patients with long-term conditions for this purpose and will work with the Long-term Conditions Alliance to agree the way forward.

The Government accepts in principle the Committee's recommendation to ensure that HealthSpace allows patients to view audit trails, showing who has accessed their SCR and under what circumstances, and offers mechanisms for investigating inappropriate access. Facilities will be needed to enable patients to view details of who has accessed their records in line with the commitments of the Care Record Guarantee, and consideration will be given to how best to meet this and the other parts of the recommendation.

The Government also accepts the recommendation to promote the use of HealthSpace, monitor levels of uptake, and ensure that there is equitable access across the country and that coercive access is prevented. NHS Connecting for Health already monitors the levels of take-up for each primary care trust (PCT). It is intended to monitor this further by relating the levels of take-up to each type of local public-facing communications activity and to analyse the demographic details of advanced account users. NHS Connecting for Health also monitors its helpdesk activity for reports of coercive access, though to date none have been received.

The Government agrees in principle with the Committee's recommendation for an independent evaluation of HealthSpace once it is widely available.

Recommendation (paragraph 123)

We note that in France patients will own their national summary record. This approach gives patients more control over who can access their record and more opportunity to influence and take control of their own care. We therefore recommend that Connecting for Health consider a similar model for the SCR in England.

The Government accepts the principle of patient control of a national SCR and HealthSpace will be a key enabler in this process. However, the Government is unable to accept that the means to achieve this is to put control of the record through a separate health insurance card.

The fundamental differences in funding method between the French and English healthcare systems require different models. The French system requires patients to authorise access to their Personal Health Record (PHR) using their health insurance card. This is driven in part by the fundamentally insurance-based French healthcare system; treatment is not free at the point of delivery of care, in contrast to the English system, and the patient pays for treatment, reclaiming the cost from insurance funds (generally the state insurance scheme). The fundamental rationale is therefore that any (non-emergency) treatment requires the specific authorisation of the patient, whereas in the UK funding is a background process handled internally by the NHS and invisible to the patient. In the UK, the fact of registration with a GP practice is the basic authority for access to the health record and payment for any treatment.

Although there are some specific differences between the French PHR and the English SCR (for example, the 'dual card' approach), the controls over access to the information stored are similar in the two systems in that:

- both have concepts of 'role-based access', that is what information a clinician can see depends on their specific role, for example doctor, nurse, etc;

- information in the PHR can be 'hidden' at the patient's request and only made available on the patient's specific authorisation (equivalent to the 'sealed envelope');

- only authorised clinicians can enter health information (patients can add their own additional notes);

- there is provision for clinician access without patient authority in an emergency; and

- the French cards use electronic signatures to authenticate users in a manner comparable with cards issued to healthcare professionals by the National Programme.

The Government believes, therefore, that the safeguards for patients are in fact similar in both countries but that the differences in the systems necessarily reflect differences in the way healthcare is provided.

Recommendation (paragraph 125)

However, serious concerns were expressed regarding the lack of information both about how security systems will work and about the outcomes of security testing. We agree with these concerns and recommend that Connecting for Health ensure that BT's planned security systems for its national applications are subject to independent evaluation and that the outcomes of this are made public.

The Government accepts the major part of this recommendation. It accepts and already complies with the principle of independent testing by specialist third-party organisations and evaluation of security arrangements. However, it does not agree that the detail of the outcome should be made public as there would be a risk of compromising security arrangements and, potentially, criminal exploitation of information if details of the testing became public.

The National Programme has adopted the highest levels of security. The National Programme's contracts require suppliers to comply with comprehensive and detailed security requirements including security penetration testing and compliance with international standards (ISO-27001). Suppliers are obliged to report **any** breach of the security requirements and to make recommendations for the remedy of any breach. NHS Connecting for Health may call in a third party to monitor its suppliers and make reasonable recommendations in the event of a breach and/or escalate the matter for dispute resolution if the remedy proposed by the supplier is not acceptable. In the event of a breach of security incapable of remedy or that is not remedied, NHS Connecting for Health has the right to terminate the relevant contract immediately without paying compensation to the supplier.

Security testing of national applications is therefore already subject to independent evaluation and conclusions are acted upon.

Recommendation (paragraph 126)

Maintaining the operational security of the new SCR system is a substantial challenge. We acknowledge that Connecting for Health and its suppliers have made significant efforts to minimise the risk of operational security breaches. Individual smartcards, rigorous user authentication, role-based access controls, legitimate relationships and audit trails will all help to increase operational security, both individually and in combination. However, many of these measures are new and untested on the scale that they will be used in the NHS. As a result, their impact and vulnerabilities are difficult to predict. We therefore recommend that Connecting for Health:

- **Ensure that the evaluation of the early adopter sites examines both the individual and the collective impact of the new operational security measures for the SCR, commissioning a separate evaluation if necessary; and**

- **Undertake a program of operational security training for all staff with access to the SCR, emphasising the importance of not divulging information to those who request it under false pretexts.**

The Government welcomes the recognition of the work done by NHS Connecting for Health and its suppliers to minimise risks and accepts the Committee's recommendations. The Government confirms that the evaluation of the early adopter sites will include an assessment of the impact of the operational security measures for the SCR. Emerging findings from the evaluation will feed into the further implementation of the SCR within early adopter communities and will also inform the national implementation of the SCR from 2008 onwards.

As part of the early adopter programme, a rolling programme of training is in place for all NHS staff on security and confidentiality issues of the SCR. This is in addition to routine training on the use of IT, data protection and confidentiality requirements for patient information. Relevant lessons from the evaluation will be incorporated.

Recommendation (paragraph 127)

Operational security also depends on effective enforcement. The Department of Health and the Information Commissioner's Office have called for custodial sentences for people who unlawfully access personal information. The Committee welcomes this, and recommends that a substantial audit resource be provided to detect and prosecute those who access the system unlawfully.

The Government accepts the principle of this recommendation and believes that the necessary processes for prosecution are in place. NHS Connecting for Health has supported the Information Commissioner's call for custodial sentences for unlawful access to personal information to strengthen the deterrent.

NHS Connecting for Health places the highest importance on safeguarding patient information through numerous information governance controls within the systems deployed and information assurance practices across all organisations using the National Programme's digital services. NHS Connecting for Health works closely with the Department of Health and the Healthcare Commission to ensure that healthcare organisations using National Programme systems maintain standards to ensure that patient information is not accessed unlawfully.

Organisations and individuals using systems supplied by NHS Connecting for Health must abide by set conditions controlling access to and use of those systems. These mechanisms, which are already in place, ensure that only appropriately authorised NHS personnel, with an appropriate role and an established legitimate relationship with the patient, can access confidential patient information in the NHS. Compliance with these organisational and individual obligations is monitored regularly using online assessment tools and a national audit framework; alerts are generated automatically when attempts are made to transgress these controls.

In some exceptional cases, access controls to patient information can be overridden due to a court order, access by statute or in the public interest. In these cases, alerts are raised through the system to the nominated privacy officer, who will ensure that the action taken by the user is justified and lawful.

Recommendation (paragraph 229)

Yet there is a perplexing lack of clarity about exactly what NPfIT (National Programme for IT) will now deliver. It is not clear what information will be recorded and shared on DCR (Detailed Care Record) systems, nor the range of organisations that will be able to share information. Suppliers told us there will be significant variation between the size of different areas. The Department stated that DCR systems may be confined to areas as small as a single hospital or as large as an entire SHA. While local control over the new systems is a desirable goal, it is surprising that the architects of the DCR were not able to provide a clearer vision of what is planned. There is an explanatory vacuum surrounding DCR systems and this must be addressed if duplication of effort at a local level is to be avoided. We recommend that Connecting for Health:

- **Publish clear information about its plans for DCR systems, stating in particular what area will be covered by shared records and what degree of information sharing will be possible; these plans should make reference to the original specifications for the Integrated Care Records Service, making clear how the scope of the project has changed since 2003; and**

- **Set out clear milestones for achieving the increasing levels of interoperability and automation offered by DCR systems.**

The Government accepts these recommendations. There have been changes to NHS organisational boundaries and a review of the information-sharing arrangements is already under way with strategic health authorities (SHAs) and suppliers. This aims to ensure that the patient benefits from information sharing across care settings are preserved while also ensuring resilience and flexibility for organisational purposes and local management reporting. The evaluation of the SCR will be helpful in establishing future plans.

A maturity model of secondary care settings already exists which describes the opportunities for moving from systems being linked simply by interfaces to interoperable systems that can move patient data between national, local and existing departmental systems, and ultimately to fully integrated systems. Suppliers are being asked to map their proposals against the maturity model with key milestone dates.

Recommendation (paragraph 233)

We recommend that Connecting for Health:

- **Ensure that all LSPs publish detailed timetables for delivering new PAS [Patient Administration System] applications, electronic prescribing systems and shared local record systems, indicating what level of information sharing will be possible when DCRs are first implemented; and**

- **Set a deadline for the successful deployment of the Lorenzo system in an NHS hospital, making clear that if the deadline is not achieved then other systems with similar capability will be offered to local hospitals.**

The Government accepts these recommendations. Initially, the National Programme developed detailed implementation plans covering a long forward period but a combination of factors, including software development, implementation issues and NHS operational needs, led to changed dates and uncertainty. Experience shows that, when a trust is maintaining essential patient services during an implementation, there must be some flexibility and movement in dates to account for local circumstances. Following the report by the National Audit Office, the approach has been modified. Responsibility for deployment, including planning and timetabling, has now been transferred to the local NHS, who agree the deployments with suppliers in line with the suppliers' capacity and their local NHS business circumstances and implementation slots. This ensures that local circumstances are taken into account and both the NHS and suppliers are involved in deployment decisions. This is therefore removing much of the earlier uncertainty for trusts.

Although the delays to the delivery of the Lorenzo system have been disappointing for the NHS, deployments are scheduled for early adopter sites in the summer of 2008. Recent demonstrations of the Lorenzo product to NHS clinicians and managers confirm that it meets the requirements and expectations of the NHS and provides improved confidence that the current planned timetable will be achieved. The NHS and suppliers are working together to ensure that Lorenzo can be delivered within the terms and life of the contract.

Recommendation (paragraph 234)

In light of a range of concerns, including the delays to elements of the DCR programme, a number of witnesses called for an independent review of the whole of NPfIT. Whilst we understand the reasons for this, we do not agree that a comprehensive review is the best way forward. First, many of the questions raised by the supporters of a review would be addressed if Connecting for Health provided the additional information and independent evaluation which we recommend in this report. Secondly, the programme has already been scrutinised by the National Audit Office, the Public Accounts Committee and ourselves. We therefore recommend that:

- **The implementation of DCR systems be addressed in the short term by increasing both the local ownership and the professional leadership of the programme; and**

- **The ongoing review by Lord Darzi on the future of the NHS include in its remit the long-term prospects for using electronic systems to improve the quality of care, particularly for the growing number of patients with long-term conditions.**

The Government is pleased that the Committee recognises that a comprehensive review of the Programme at this stage is not necessary and accepts fully the recommendations.

Local ownership is now being achieved through the NPfIT Local Ownership Programme (NLOP) initiated by the Chief Executive of the NHS in September 2006. Under NLOP, SHA chief executives became accountable as senior responsible owners (SROs) for the implementation of DCR systems in their SHA from April 2007. Governance processes are now in place to ensure that system requirements and deployment plans are developed and owned at local level with professional leadership and expertise in commercial management, IT and programme management being provided by NHS Connecting for Health. The London Programme for IT (LPfIT), the Southern Programme for IT (SPfIT) and the North, Midlands and East Programme for IT (NMEPfIT) each have programme directors now in place to improve the professional leadership of the Programme at a local level for each supplier. Local ownership is also addressing the issues of standardisation and common ways of working while, at the same time, catering for specific local NHS needs. This will address some of the problems that the NHS and suppliers have experienced over a lack of standardised processes to date.

Following the publication of Lord Darzi's interim report, *Our NHS Our Future*, the NHS Chief Executive has ordered a review of information across the health service. Recent investment in technology in the NHS has created the opportunity to make a step change in how the NHS uses information. The NPfIT has connected every hospital and GP surgery to a common secure network. Clinicians now see benefits from the implementation of digital access to X-rays and scans (PACS) and new IT systems are going into primary, community and hospital settings.

However, while the NHS has a great deal of data, it lacks meaningful information. Much of the information is available to limited numbers of people, often inconsistent with that held elsewhere, and frequently not available at the point of need. A key part of the review will be to bring together the data collected by the NHS and other organisations to maximise value, reduce any bureaucracy and ensure that patients, staff and the public can access the information they need. This is not a specific review of the NPfIT or of NHS Connecting for Health. It is a broader investigation into how the NHS can improve the collection and sharing of information – including statistics, performance data and patient information, including long-term care – to improve the quality of healthcare for patients.

Recommendation (paragraph 236)

There are already signs of a change of approach to increase local ownership of system implementation. Accountability is being devolved through the NPfIT Local Ownership Programme and control for some users is being increased through GP Systems of Choice. These measures are welcome but overdue. There is a need to go further and faster with reforms of this type. We recommend that:

- **Connecting for Health devolve responsibility for performance managing implementation of all NPfIT systems to Strategic Health Authorities (SHAs);**

- **SHAs devolve responsibility for operational deployment by giving individual hospital trusts control over implementing their own new systems. SHAs should also devolve responsibility for implementing shared record systems across local health communities to their constituent Primary Care Trusts (PCTs);**

- **SHAs, PCTs and hospital trusts be given the authority to negotiate directly with LSPs and to hold suppliers to account, so that local organisations are not given responsibility without power; and**

- **Connecting for Health offer all local organisations a choice of systems from a catalogue of accredited suppliers, as far as this approach is possible within the limitations of existing contracts.**

The Government accepts the first of these recommendations. As already stated, SHAs now have accountability for managing implementation of the IT systems provided by local service providers. In respect of the national applications (for example, the N3), accountability remains with NHS Connecting for Health.

The second recommendation is assumed to relate to responsibilities for the implementation of applications provided under the National Programme's contractual arrangements. In this respect, the Government considers that the devolution of responsibilities by SHAs, to individual hospital trusts and PCTs, is a matter for determination by the local NHS within the existing governance arrangements that have been developed to support the local ownership programme.

The spirit of the third recommendation is met by individual PCTs and hospital trusts being able to deal directly with suppliers in respect of implementations and being responsible for signing off systems at a local level before payment is made. The programme directors for the South, London, and the North, East and Midlands are responsible for dealing directly with suppliers in respect of requirements and wider planning across SHAs. NHS Connecting for Health remains responsible for commercial matters within the governance of the South, London, and North, East and Midlands Programme Boards.

There is no intention to change the contractual arrangements. The central procurement exercise and management focus are the foundations for the work done so far and the value for money that the contracts offer, as well as achieving the technical requirements for interoperability. Through the NLOP, the Department of Health will ensure that SHAs, PCTs and trusts, working together with NHS Connecting for Health, are in a position to hold their local service providers to account and participate fully in negotiations with them.

The fourth recommendation is partly met by GP Systems of Choice and there are already over 100 existing IT systems that have been accredited to link with national and local systems within the programme. Within the limits of the contracts and available resources, NHS Connecting for Health will continue to work with suppliers of existing systems to extend accreditation and compliance and to publicise the current status of accredited suppliers.

Recommendations (paragraphs 237 and 238)

Connecting for Health's own role should switch as soon as possible to focus on setting and ensuring compliance with technical and clinical standards for NHS IT systems, rather than presiding over local implementation. Clear standards would allow systems to be accredited nationally but would also ensure that local trusts have a choice of system and control over implementation.

Technical standards should cover system security and reliability but should focus in particular on ensuring full interoperability between accredited systems. Comprehensive interoperability standards should guarantee that data can be seamlessly exchanged between systems whilst ensuring that users are not committed to a single supplier. In order to develop transparent technical standards, we recommend that Connecting for Health:

- **Establish an independent technical standards body responsible for setting the interoperability requirements for data exchange for all systems deployed in the NHS. These standards should be published and subjected to full external scrutiny;**

- **Require all system suppliers to the NHS to meet and demonstrate conformity with these standards. Systems should be "kite marked" or classified to give details of their compatibility; and**
- **Work with industry and academia to establish an independent technical standards testing service to evaluate and accredit systems for use in the NHS.**

Much of what the Committee proposes is already in place. Devolvement of accountability to SHAs for implementation of the National Programme's systems means that NHS Connecting for Health is no longer presiding over local implementation.

NHS Connecting for Health already focuses on setting and ensuring compliance with technical and clinical standards for NHS IT systems. The creation of The Messaging Service (TMS) as an atomic approach to record generation as part of the Spine architecture has been key to enabling over 100 million messages per month to be handled effectively across the systems. The use of standard HL7v3 messages throughout the systems has been a fundamental enabler. Only compliant systems that are approved and accredited are permitted to connect to the Spine. NHS Connecting for Health's National Integration Centre provides the main compliance mechanism to demonstrate integration of national, local and existing systems and assures the testing of systems that integrate via the NHS National Spine. This assurance covers not only the technical implementation, but also the patient safety and business practices of the organisation that is seeking compliance. These arrangements provide a comprehensive perspective on interoperability standards and promote development of those standards. NHS Connecting for Health, for example, has taken a leading role in establishing and developing the International Health Terminology Standards Development Organisation (IHTSDO) to secure the long-term strategic effectiveness of Systematized Nomenclature of Medicine (Clinical Terms) (SNOMED CT) terminology not just for the NHS but for the broader UK and international community.

An independent standards body is in place. The Information Standards Board (ISB) is responsible for assuring and ensuring NHS information standards. These standards are published and subjected to full external scrutiny by a broad range of expertise, including clinical and academic reviewers independent of the programmes of work that deliver applications using the standards and independent of the standards' development process. There is a contractual requirement for suppliers to utilise ISB-approved standards.

The Government believes that these arrangements meet the recommendations and already involve industry, academia and professional bodies. It should be remembered that progress on the electronic health record on a national basis was virtually non-existent until the Programme was established and substantial numbers of deployments have been achieved since.

Recommendation (paragraph 239)

Safe and effective data sharing, the fundamental aim of DCR systems, also requires a more standardised approach to the recording of clinical information. Such an approach is at the heart of ensuring real interoperability between systems and is vital if data from DCR systems is to be used as a basis either for the SCR or for research. The NHS Data Dictionary and the SNOMED CT coding system are important to achieving more consistent recording of patient information. We recommend that Connecting for Health publish a timetable for introducing SNOMED CT across the NHS.

The Government welcomes the Committee's support for the approach already taken by NHS Connecting for Health to lead the establishment of SNOMED CT as an international standard for healthcare applications. SNOMED CT is a requirement in all new NHS IT developments and is also mandated in the specifications published by NHS Connecting for Health for ensuring interoperability between new and existing systems.

The initiative taken by NHS Connecting for Health to establish an International SNOMED Standards Development Organisation has ensured that SNOMED CT is available free of charge to all suppliers in the UK, and electronic distribution of the international release and the UK extensions has been available since June 2007.

However, the widespread implementation of SNOMED CT across the NHS needs to be staged to demonstrate the use of the terminology in a number of operational NHS settings. The Department, therefore, cannot yet publish a timetable for the introduction of SNOMED CT across the NHS until clinically proven and safe DCR systems are available.

Recommendation (paragraph 240)

But Connecting for Health must do much more to ensure that the recording of detailed clinical data is standardised. Professionally developed datasets and agreed approaches to the structure and content of detailed records are urgently needed for each of the main clinical specialties and for use in a range of different care settings. Developing such standards will require close collaboration with Royal Colleges and other professional bodies. We recommend that Connecting for Health work with professional groups to:

- **Identify the information standards which will be required within their specialty area; and**

- **Develop and implement consensus-based clinical information standards.**

The Government accepts these recommendations. NHS Connecting for Health is working with professional clinical groups to develop standards for clinical records, including comprehensive clinically assured definitions. This follows a successful pilot investigation into the use of the European Committee for Standardisation (CEN) 13606 standard. Since February 2007, NHS Connecting for Health has been using the developed models to assist the definition of clinical content for iSOFT applications. These models will provide the basis for a common set of models for the NHS.

Recommendation (paragraph 241)

Separate clinical records on an individual patient can only be combined safely if each person can be accurately identified. The introduction of the new NHS number as the unique patient identifier and its allocation at birth through NHS Numbers for Babies is therefore a significant achievement. Yet the value of this work and the future integrity of clinical information will be undermined if organisations are unable to retrieve an individual's NHS number when they need to use it or to allocate temporary NHS numbers for use in emergencies. We recommend that:

- **The Department of Health set a timetable for mandating the use of the correct NHS number on all clinical communications, and make this a performance measure for all NHS organisations;**

- **Processes are introduced to allow temporary NHS numbers to be allocated which can subsequently be reconciled with the patient's permanent NHS number through the Personal Demographic Service; and**

- **Systems are maintained to treat patients under a separate, pseudonymous NHS number where this is necessary.**

The Government welcomes the Committee's recognition of the importance of the work done so far and, in respect of the three recommendations:

- It accepts in principle the first recommendation about the use of the NHS number. The introduction of the National Programme has provided the impetus for wider use of the NHS number. The National Programme Board has confirmed that use of the NHS number should be standard. The ISB has accepted this in principle and NHS Connecting for Health is working with it and the NHS on the development of implementation plans.

- It accepts the second of these recommendations. The Personal Demographics Service has provided the facility for allocating NHS numbers since January 2006. Processes for ensuring that temporary NHS numbers can be reconciled with patients' permanent numbers are now operational across all PCTs, following the completion of implementation in September 2007. This has reduced the lead time for reconciliation of duplicate NHS numbers from several weeks to around two or three days.

- The Government also accepts the third of these recommendations. The NHS Care Records Service specification already includes the requirement to provide, where appropriate, a facility to record anonymously a patient's attendance.

Recommendation (paragraph 242)

The resilience of new systems will be enhanced by distributing data across a range of hosting centres. Suppliers assured us that systems will be distributed in this way but the impact of the power failure at the Maidstone data centre, which affected 80 trusts, suggests otherwise. We recognise that lessons have been learned from the Maidstone incident. Nonetheless, we recommend that Connecting for Health instruct suppliers to publish details of all significant reliability problems along with a full incident log.

The Government considers that the principle of this recommendation is already met through the regular publication of system availability information. Details of service reliability are shared regularly with SHA representatives. However, the Government does not accept that the wider publication of full incident logs represents industry practice and the technical detail would add no value to the public understanding.

The IT systems and services deployed by NHS Connecting for Health have proved to be highly resilient, and statistics on service performance and availability are published regularly on NHS Connecting for Health's website, something that is virtually unique among IT service providers. NHS Connecting for Health also works with suppliers and NHS organisations to maintain coordinated business continuity plans against the risk of service failures.

Suppliers are obliged to produce reports detailing significant reliability problems for NHS Connecting for Health, which are subsequently shared with SHAs and other key stakeholders in the NHS, but there is no intention to publish them more widely. Individual reports are incorporated into a monthly report for each supplier and are used to improve services. These reports are also shared with SHA representatives.

Given the proven high resilience of the systems, the Government does not agree that there is a need to change the current procedures.

Recommendation (paragraph 243)

The sharing of unique smartcards between users is unacceptable and undermines the operational security of DCR systems. However, we sympathise with the A&E staff who shared smartcards when faced with waits of a minute or more to access their new PAS software. Unless unacceptably lengthy log-on times are addressed, security breaches are inevitable. We recommend that Connecting for Health:

- **Ensure that suppliers have clear plans for achieving access times compatible with realistic clinical requirements for all of their systems; and**

- **Continue to monitor the potential for introducing more sophisticated access systems, such as facial pattern recognition, in busy areas such as A&E.**

The Government accepts the first of these recommendations. In recent months, NHS Connecting for Health and local service providers have continued to work on a number of initiatives to improve access times, including:

- faster smartcard authentication software, which is available to the NHS for installation now and is about 60% faster than the original version, allowing log-on to the Spine in four or five seconds routinely;

- a series of application changes to remove unnecessary screens and mouse clicks from the application start-up;

- a secure solution, which is being installed to allow removal and reinsertion of the smartcard without stopping the user's applications;

- a different architectural design in Lorenzo, which will improve log-on and start-up processes; and

- the increased use of mobile devices which will allow staff to log-on once and keep their device with them. NHS Connecting for Health has been working with industry to define a mobile computer that is designed around the needs of clinicians. The first is now in production, as the Mobile Clinical Assistant (MCA) being produced by Phillips and Motion Computing, and other vendors will follow. The design of the MCA was based on input from thousands of clinicians to simplify workflow and improve efficiency.

The Government accepts the principle of the second of these recommendations. However, NHS Connecting for Health has reviewed alternative technologies to validate staff identity, such as facial, retinal and fingerprint recognition, and concluded that these are not yet sufficiently mature to operate securely in clinical settings. These technologies will be kept under review.

Recommendation (paragraph 244)

The Department has indicated that explicit consent will be required before DCR information can be shared between separate organisations. The Committee supports this approach and recommends that the consent model for the shared DCR be communicated to patients as clearly and as early as possible.

The Government does not accept the premise on which this recommendation is based. However, the Government recognises the importance of ensuring that local NHS organisations inform patients effectively about how information is used and shared and that NHS Connecting for Health provides support and guidance, including model communication material and toolkits. It therefore accepts the actual recommendation that the consent model for the shared DCR be communicated as clearly and as early as possible.

As the Department of Health confirmed in its written evidence to the Committee: 'The NHS has always operated on an opt-out or implied consent basis for sharing information about patients. What will change with the introduction of the new systems is that when patients request that information is not shared, it won't be'. (EPR01A, paragraph 19)

Patients will have a number of options, including 'to direct that controls are set to prevent data sharing. In this case the SCR can only be viewed with the individual's express permission or in accordance with the exceptions to English common law confidentiality obligations. Local sharing of Detailed Care Records across organisational boundaries will also be prevented essentially recreating the pre-NCRS. situation.' (EPR01, paragraph 44(ii))

The *NHS Code of Practice on Confidentiality*, published in November 2003 with the support of the Information Commissioner, the General Medical Council and the British Medical Association, set out the policy position. Where patients have been informed of the use and disclosure of their information for healthcare purposes, the choices that they have and the implications of choosing to restrict how information may be used or shared, then explicit consent is not generally required for information to be shared to provide that healthcare.

Information sharing across and between NHS organisations for healthcare purposes is not new. It is a necessary component of an effective care process and is not a result of the introduction of the DCR. Indeed, various other types of DCR have been in existence in isolated health communities for a number of years. What the National Programme will provide is a more coherent and comprehensive DCR which will ensure that all patients of the NHS in England can benefit from their clinicians having access to the information that they need.

Although explicit consent is not required to support DCR information sharing between organisations, patients who wish to prevent this may do so by requesting that information sharing is 'turned off' in their particular case. In time, when sealed envelopes are widely available, patients will be able to choose to share some, none or all of the information in their DCRs.

Recommendation (paragraph 245)

However, if sensitive information is to be stored and shared on DCR systems, it is important that local "sealed envelope" systems are developed and tested as soon as possible. We were concerned to hear that suppliers have not yet received specifications for local "sealed envelopes". We recommend that Connecting for Health provide such specifications as a matter of urgency and set a clear timetable for the introduction of this technology at a local level.

The Government accepts the Committee's recommendation. NHS Connecting for Health issued a detailed specification for local sealed envelopes to its suppliers on 3 April 2007. A timetable will be set as soon as practicable.

Recommendation (paragraph 281)

The Department has acknowledged the need to take advantage of the research opportunities offered by the SUS and has established a partnership with the UK Clinical Research Collaboration to achieve this. We welcome this, but researchers nevertheless told us that much more could be done to maximise these opportunities. We recommend that Connecting for Health:

- **Mandate the use of the unique patient identifier, the NHS number, in all health service interactions in England;**

- **Develop appropriate linkage between databases within and beyond the SUS. This would also have benefits for non-research activities such as health protection;**

- **Ensure that the development of clinical information standards, which we recommended in Chapter 4, takes account of the needs of research; and**

- **Initiate a campaign of public engagement so that both the opportunities and risks from using health data for research purposes are better understood.**

The Government is committed to supporting the research opportunities afforded by the NHS Care Records Service and specifically the Secondary Uses Service (SUS). The partnership with the UK Clinical Research Collaboration (UKCRC, a partnership of organisations working to establish the UK as a world leader in clinical research, by harnessing the power of the NHS; see www.ukcrc.org/) is now being progressed.

In particular, the Government:

- accepts the recommendation to mandate the use of the NHS number. More information is provided in the response to recommendation paragraph 241;

- accepts the recommendation about developing appropriate linkage between databases and has established the Research Capability Programme which will investigate the effectiveness of the pseudonymisation process, the role of safe havens and third-party brokers, and the appropriate governance arrangements for access to data for research purposes;

- accepts the recommendation to ensure that the development of clinical standards takes account of the needs of research; and

- accepts the recommendation for specific public engagement to assess the level of understanding and support among the public for the objectives of secondary uses of health data and for the proposed levels of security and confidentiality when identifiable information is used for purposes other than direct care. The Research Capability Programme includes plans for such engagement.

Recommendation (paragraph 284)

There is an urgent need to address these problems, especially as the amount and type of data potentially available through the SUS will proliferate rapidly in future. We recommend that the Department of Health conduct a review of both national and local procedures for controlling access to electronic health data for "secondary" uses. In particular, the review should examine:

- **How best to balance the opportunity to improve access to data for research purposes with the ongoing need to safeguard patient privacy;**

- **Whether to establish a national Information Governance Board to oversee the arrangements for access to data for secondary uses;**

- **The case for establishing a permanent body to succeed the Patient Information Advisory Group and whether this should be a subcommittee of the national Board;**

- **The effectiveness of the pseudonymisation process proposed by Connecting for Health and its suppliers, which should be subject to independent public evaluation;**

- **What compensating controls, such as third party brokerage, should be used to protect patient privacy in situations where research must be conducted with partially rather than fully pseudonymised information; and**

- **How governance arrangements for access to data for research purposes should differ from those which apply to other "secondary" purposes, such as immigration and counter-terrorism.**

The Government accepts these recommendations. It agrees with the many organisations and individuals that provided evidence to the Committee that the very existence of the SUS provides opportunities for significant healthcare benefits for the population as a whole. However, it recognises the importance of balancing the opportunity to improve access to electronic health data for secondary uses with the need for patient privacy and has already taken steps that will address the recommendations.

Plans to establish a new National Information Governance Board were already in hand and it met for the first time in October 2007. This body will oversee all aspects of the use of patient information in health and social care, including for research and other secondary purposes. Initially, the National Information Governance Board will take over the functions of the Care Record Development Board (CRDB) but its overall remit will be wider than that of the CRDB. Should the National Information Governance Board become a statutory body in the future, it will, subject to legislation, take over the statutory functions of the Patient Information Advisory Group.

Following the commitment in the Government health strategy *Best Research for Best Health*, the UKCRC advisory group has been looking at these issues. This work will involve all key stakeholders and will be conducted openly and collaboratively.

The Department of Health has initiated a programme of work (the Research Capability Programme) that will investigate the effectiveness of the pseudonymisation process, the role of safe havens and third-party brokers, and the appropriate governance arrangements for access to data for research purposes.

The governance arrangements that apply to research already differ considerably from those that apply to purposes such as immigration and counter-terrorism. The new National Information Governance Board will consider whether these arrangements require strengthening and whether current guidance on disclosure for non-research secondary uses requires revision.

Printed in the UK for The Stationery Office Limited
on behalf of the Controller of Her Majesty's Stationery Office
ID5696160 11/07

Printed on paper containing 75% recycled fibre content minimum.